The

Book of

MYSTERIES

Written by Lou Silverstone
Illustrated by Jack Rickard

Edited by Nick Meglin

WARNER BOOKS

A Warner Communications Company

WARNER BOOKS EDITION

Copyright © **1980** by Lou Silverstone, Jack Rickard,
and E.C. Publications, Inc.

This Warner Books Edition is published by
arrangement with E.C. Publications, Inc.

Warner Books, Inc.,
75 Rockefeller Plaza,
New York, N.Y. 10019

Ⓦ A Warner Communications Company

Printed in the United States of America

First Printing: August, 1980

10   9   8   7   6   5   4   3   2   1

CONTENTS

THE KING PUTZ MURDER

A HERCULES
PIROUETTE
MYSTERY

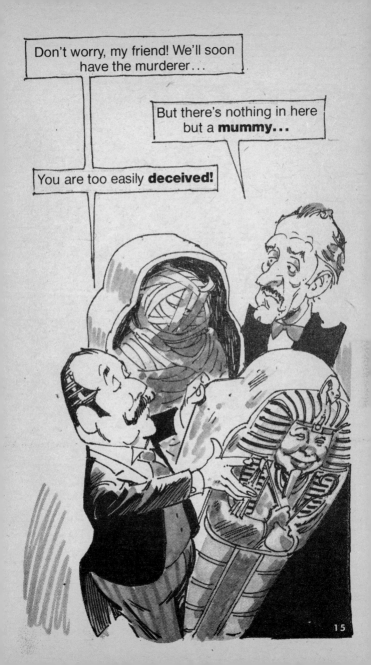

I have definitely concluded that the murderer is **not** hiding in the mummy case! Now I would like to ask you all some questions! Did any of you know the deceased?
NERO WOLFE
Jack Rickard

26

21

23

25

It would be a complete mystery to have an incomplete mystery book— and no mystery book would be complete without a tough-talking, cynical private eye...

The Fershluginer Falcon

From the Files of
**ARCHER
SPILLANE
SPAYED**

CHAPTER I

"My name is Archer Spillane Spayed. I'm a private eye. With a name like that what'd you expect, a dental technician?" I said.

The bartender, who looked like he just got back from trick or treating and forgot to remove his mask didn't hear me. He was watching the news on the tube.

"The body of an oriental, identified as Who Flung Dung, a curio dealer, was found murdered late this evening. He had been dead for several days," said the news commentator.

"Good riddance," grunted the bartender, switching off the idiot box. He turned in my direction and mumbled something.

I didn't understand him. "Play it again, Sam," I quipped.

"Look, shmuck, you wanna drink? It's almos' closin' time."

I threw a quick glance at my watch, it was either a quarter past three or one of the hands had dropped off. I tipped my hat to a rakish angle, snapped my fingers and crooned, "It's a quarter past three… ain't no one in the place except you and me… so set 'em up, Joe…."

"Cheez," groaned the barkeep, "I get 'em all in this joint!"

The next sound I heard was a dull 'gonk'. That was the noise my head makes whenever it comes into contact with a .45. When I get slugged with a .38, it makes a more resounding sound… 'Krunch!'. This was definitely a .45, I thought. Then everything went black.

CHAPTER II

When I came to, my head was throbbing like the Stones were doing a wild gig and using my skull for a drum. I hummed along for a few bars and then opened my eyes. Staring me in the face was a blunt nosed .45. It was being held by a creep dressed in early Richard Widmark; black shirt and white tie. Man, I thought, if it weren't for the Late Show, these punks wouldn't know how to dress.

I heard a voice say, "Spayed… " The voice belonged to a fat guy wearing a white suit. Why do fat guys always wear white suits? I mean, if he wore a small check, he wouldn't look so bloody fat.

"How are you feeling, my friend?" asked the fat man.

"Well," I replied, "my head is throbbing like the Stones were doing a wild gig…"

"Shaddup," hissed the creep, shoving the gun closer to my face.

"Spayed, we want the bird," said Fatso.

I didn't have the foggiest idea of what he was talking about. I had been in plenty of these tight situations; I had to stall for time. "I haven't got it," I said.

The Widmark clone rapped me across the choppers. He was wearing brass knuckles. "Wilmer," said the fat guy, "that's no way to treat a guest."

I had to agree with the fat boy even though technically I wasn't a guest. The fat man's voice grew cold. I felt a chill as he said, "Kill him, politely!"

CHAPTER III

They wanted the bird but I didn't have the bird. I didn't even know what the hell the bird was. But they didn't know that I didn't know that. I had to stall for more time. I gave them the old reliable, "It's in a locker in the bus terminal." Did you ever wonder why you can never find an empty locker in a bus terminal? It's because every guy that pulls a job stashes the hot merchandise in those lockers!

"Give me the key, Spayed."

They bought my bus terminal shtick! "I gave it to a friend for safekeeping and if anything happens to me, baby, the key goes straight to the cops."

Wilmer did a Cagney twitch. "Let me kill him, boss."

"Wilmer," I explained patiently, "if you waste me, the fuzz get the bird."

He was obviously more interested in zapping me than he was in the bird. "Boss, can I plug him?" he pleaded.

The fat guy placed a restricting hand on Wilmer's shoulder. "Spayed," he said, "you can leave but you'll be hearing from me."

I drove back to the office in my souped up beetle. It had been a slow day. I'd been slugged with a .45, kidnapped, rapped in the choppers with brass knuckles… "Well," I said to myself, "it's still early, sweetheart."

CHAPTER IV

I opened my office door. A strong odor filled the air. Usually my pad smelled from stale smoke or Big Macs, this was different—it was perfume! My private eye mind and my private eye nose went to work... perfume, that means a dame, but today you can't be sure. Maybe it was *Brut*. I entered the room and felt something cold and hard pressed against my ribs. It was a nickel-plated thirty-eight.

"Spayed, I want the bird." It was a woman's voice

"Et tu, *Brut*-wearer," I answered.

"What?"

"That's Shakespeare," I explained. "See, all these guys did a number with their knives on Caesar, including his main man, Brutus..."

"The bird, or I'll blow a hole through you."

I made my move. I spun around, grabbed her by the wrist and twisted hard. I usually don't like to rough up dames but I didn't feel like having a hole blown through me. Especially before lunch.

Suddenly, I was flying through the air. I landed on the floor like a sack of potatoes. I looked up, she still had the gun. The lady was middle-aged, plump and wore support hose that wrinkled at the knee. Every private eye in the business always meets hot, ripe-bodied blondes. Me, it's always the support hose crowd!

"I'm a black belt karate," she said modestly. That figured! It had been that kind of a day....

CHAPTER V

"Where's the bird?"

"Lady, I don't have the bird, I don't like birds, in fact, I think I'll stop feeding pigeons in the park."

A look of concern crossed her face. "You must have it, I mailed it to you. I marked the packages RUSH and HANDLE WITH CARE."

Dames, I thought, they'll never learn. If you mark something RUSH, those jokers at the Post Office will delay it and if you label it HANDLE WITH CARE, they'll use it for football practice.

"It's probably been delayed in the mail," I said. "Now do me a favor and put that gun away."

She put the gun in her purse. With her body, I was glad she wasn't using a leg holster.

"Tell me about the bird."

"It's a strange story."

I sighed, "They always are, lady."

"It began five hundred years ago in the now extinct principality of Ferschlug. The Crown Prince, Filbert, had a thing for birds, he even called himself Filbert the Falcon. His loyal subjects thought he was off his bird and referred to him as Filbert the Nut. Filbert made a pair of wings out of some bird feathers and tried to fly off a cliff. They never found his body."

"You're right, that is a strange story," I said.

"I didn't even get to the strange part yet," she remarked.

CHAPTER VI

She continued, "Since there was no body, the high priest placed Filbert's crown jewels in a hollowed out statue of a falcon and buried it in the royal cemetery plot. The statue of the bird was stolen by a grave robber who was found minus his head. The bird disappeared. The bird has resurfaced periodically and the story goes that whoever has it in his possession meets a violent death."

"So, why did you mail it to me?" I asked. "If there's one thing I hate it's a violent death, especially mine."

There was a knock at the door. It was the mailman holding a package that looked like the Steelers had used for a football. BLAM BLAM BLAM!! Three sharp explosions came from my office.

Must be a backfire, I thought. No, like, what would a car be doing in my office? Maybe they were fireworks, but it wasn't the 4th of July. Hell, it wasn't even July.

I looked around. The lady who had given me the bird was lying on the floor in a pool of blood. The top of her head was blown off. She was as dead as the Sonny and Cher Show. I was right, those three BLAMS BLAMS weren't backfires or fireworks, they were gun shots!

The Fershluginer Falcon curse had struck again. And now the bird was in *my* possession!

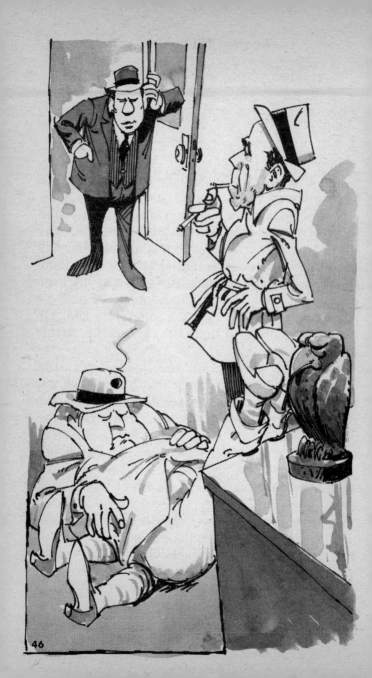

CHAPTER VII

The door to my office burst open. It was the fat man. "The bird," he cried, "you've got the bird!"

Before I could reply there were several loud reports KERSHLUG KERSHLUG! I hit the floor, so did Fatty. Unfortunately for him, he had two big holes in his belly. I wasn't a doctor but I knew a stiff when I saw one. The fat man in the white suit was as dead as the Peppermint Lounge Twist.

"What the hell are you running here, Spayed, a shooting gallery?" asked Detective Kugel of Homicide. "One more body and you win a cigar!"

Everybody's a comedian, I thought.

The cops took away the bodies. "Don't leave town, Spayed," said Detective Kugel.

I was alone with the bird and a lot of unanswered questions. Like, who was knocking people off in my office? A thing like that could give me a bad rep. I had to find the killer! "It must have something to do with you," I said to the bird.

I figured the bullets were fired from across the street. I peered out at the hotel that was directly opposite, something caught my eye, then she pulled down the shade. Then I saw a dark, metal object reflecting in the sun. It was either a king-sized licorice stick or a rifle barrel. KLABOOM KLABOOM!! It was a rifle barrel. I hit the floor, screaming in pain.

BLAM!
BLAM!

DEWAR'S

48

CHAPTER VIII

I wasn't hit, I had landed on my .45 which was tucked in my belt. I was mad, damned mad. I mean, who was going to pay for all those broken windows?

I raced across the street to the hotel. I took the elevator to the 12th floor, that's where the shots had been fired from. I wasn't sure of the room. I knocked on a door.

"Oh, my God! It's probably my wife," said a man's voice.

Wrong room. I knocked next door. "Yeah," came a familiar voice.

"Room service," I said and stepped back away from the door.

KERASH KERASH!! Two slugs ripped through the door. I squeezed the trigger of my gat...BLAM BLAM!!

"Arrrgggghhh!" came a scream from behind the door and then I heard the sound of a body hitting the floor. I kicked open the door. There on the floor, sporting a couple of brand new holes in his head, was Wilmer. He was deader than the hula hoop.

"Alright, Louie, drop the gun." It was a smirking man's voice.

Anger flooded my brain. Somebody was making fun of one of Bogie's sacred lines. I whirled, my roscoe sputtering death. A big man sagged to the floor. It was the bartender.

"Surprised?" he gasped.

"Not really, I figured it had to be you. Everybody else in this caper is already dead."

CHAPTER IX

Now that I had the case all wrapped up the police arrived, led by Detective Kugel.

"You're a little late, Kugel, I got it all wrapped up," I said.

"Cut the crap, Spayed, and tell me all about it."

"It's a strange story. It started 500 years ago with Prince Filbert..."

"Just skip the first 499 years, Spayed, I wanna know about these bodies," Kugel interrupted.

"Okay," I said, "remember back in Chapter I when the bartender was watching the news on TV? They reported an oriental art dealer killed. I figured he was knocked off because he had the bird. So Fatso and Wilmer, with the late barkeep here, pulled the job. Now they had the bird but before they could fence it, the maid at the hotel stole the bird and mailed it to me. Wilmer wasted her in my office and when Fatso tried to get the bird, Wilmer put two holes in his belly. I took out Wilmer and the bartender, and now Kugel, the bird is all yours."

Kugel scratched his head. "Spayed, that story doesn't make any sense."

I grinned. "These cases never do, sweetheart."

As I left I heard Kugel shout, "Don't leave town, Spayed." You'd think the Fuzz would come up with a new line, like, "Don't fly the coop," or "You're restricted to the area." Hell, if they had imagination they wouldn't be cops, they'd be private eyes. Or dental technicians...

AN ALLERGY QUEEN ENCOUNTER

The Mystery Of LIZZY GORY

61

67

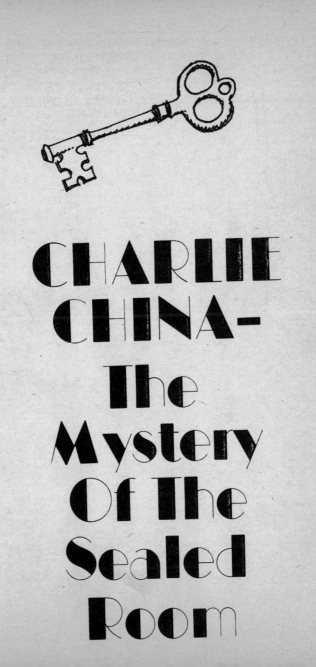

CHARLIE CHINA—

The Mystery Of The Sealed Room

It's hard to believe, but Government Undercover Agents were considered national heroes when your parents were teenagers. It's even harder to believe that your parents were teenagers! Well, they were and when they went to the movies they saw pictures like this . . .

TYPICAL G-MAN MOVIE OF THE PAST

THE NEXT MORNING...

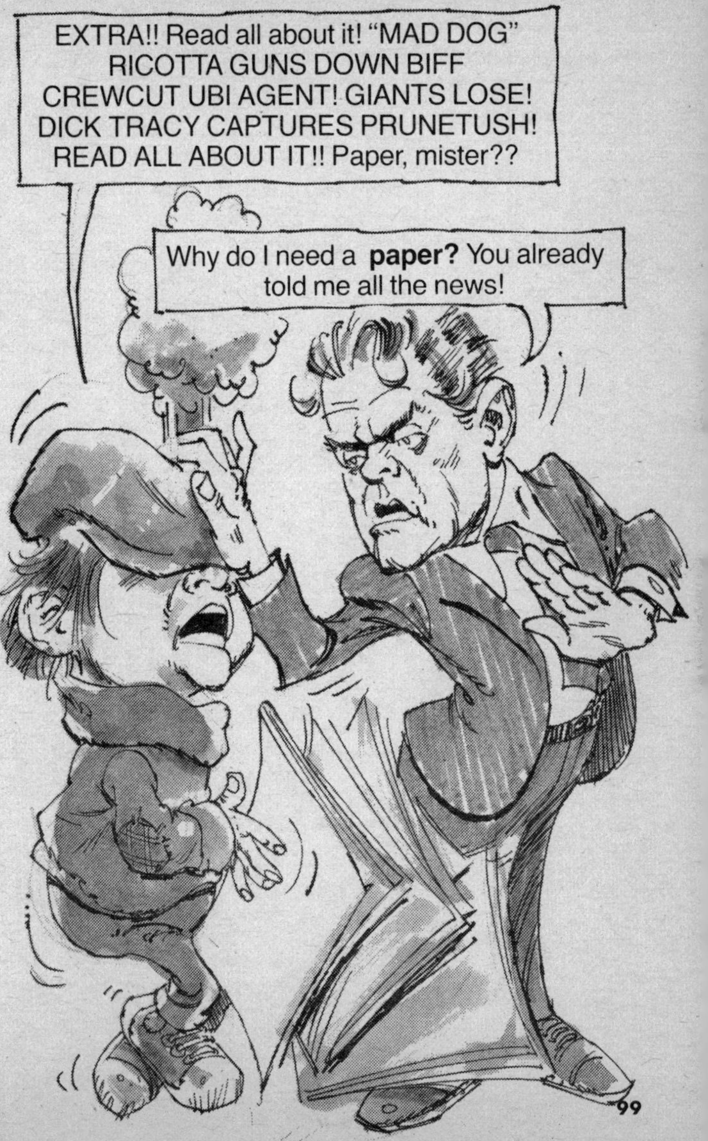

LATER YET...

EVEN LATER YET...

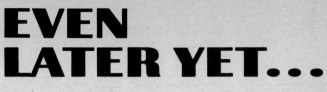

Of course, the heroic image of Federal Agents has undergone a *drastic change!* You'll see as we take a look at a typical . . .

TELL-IT-LIKE-IT-IS G-MAN MOVIE OF TODAY

115

LATER...

Only the **toughest** of you will survive this training! You're going to learn everything a law enforcement officer has to know: electronic surveillance; breaking and entering; keyhole peeping; lying to a Congressional Committee; starting a riot on campus, and stonewalling before a Grand Jury!

Frank, they just don't make agents like they used to ...

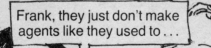

Yeah, how can anybody 'do' these guys?

EVEN LATER...

Congratulations, you are now U-Men! I'm assigning you all to **one case!** I don't want you looking for Commies or drug connections! I want you to concentrate on getting Rosebud Kane, the heiress who was kidnapped and decided to join the radicals that abducted her! I want that dirty rat!

Is she **that** big a threat to the country?

No, she's a big threat to **me!** She gets her picture in the papers more than I do!

Some things never change!

124

CHUCK FROWN
PRIVATE EYE

129

133

A
PERRY MACEFACE
ADVENTURE

"THE CASE OF THE BOUNCING BUTTOX"

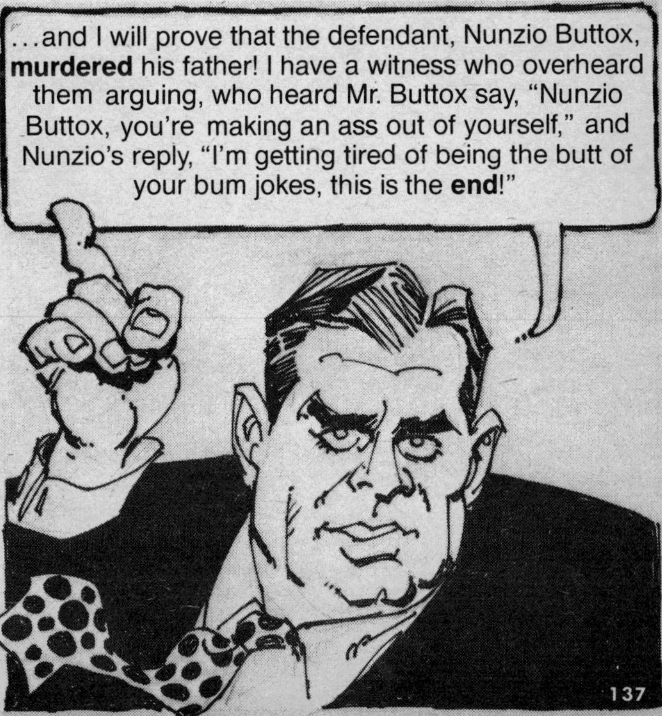

143

145

150

THE LAWMAN'S GUIDE
TO WHAT THEY SAY AND WHAT THEY MEAN

WHAT THEY SAY...

WHAT THEY MEAN...

We haven't got the foggiest idea who did it!

WHAT THEY SAY...

Chief, we advised the prisoner of his **rights!**

WHAT THEY MEAN...

And a few **lefts,** too!

155

WHAT THEY MEAN...

Man, I don't know how fast you were going, but I got to give out my quota of tickets!

Jack Rickard

WHAT THEY SAY...

I joined the force because I wanted to help make our streets safe for people!

WHAT THEY SAY...

The arrest of the perpetrator was due to good old-fashioned police work!

WHAT THEY MEAN...

From the records of Doctor Whatso, we present "*The Return of the Ripper*" another adventure in the life of

SHAMUS HOMES

In the year 1890, I was residing at 221 Baker Street with the eminent detective, Shamus Homes. It was one o'clock in the afternoon when I returned to the flat with some startling news. Homes was playing his violin…

Homes, I have some dreadful news! The Ripper struck again!

Aha, Whatso, I warned you about those newfangled zippers! They always seem to get stuck at the most inopportune time! Give me a good old-fashioned button fly anytime!

SKREEK

170

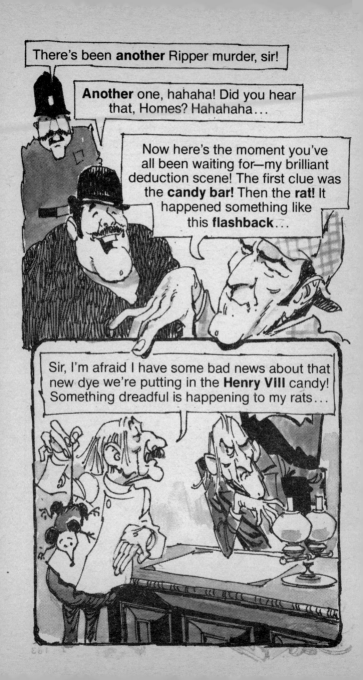

183

191